How did I get here?

PHILIP BUNTING

wren
&rook

Let's start at the beginning
(or at least what we think is the beginning).

Once upon a time, our entire universe
fit into a space smaller than an orange.

In those days, there wasn't much to see
around here. No light, no stars, no Earth.

Until one day ...

there was a really, really, really, big ...

Bang!

In about the time it takes to eat
an ice-cream, all of the bits that
make up our universe were created.

This is the stuff we're all made from.

You, me, this book, your lunch ... we're all
made of particles that have been around
since the beginning of time.

As they floated through the universe, some of
these particles began to bump into one another.
A few enjoyed each other's company so much
that they decided to stick together.

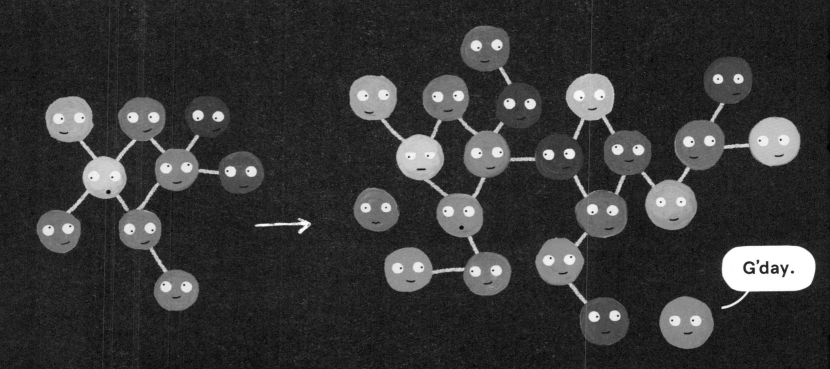

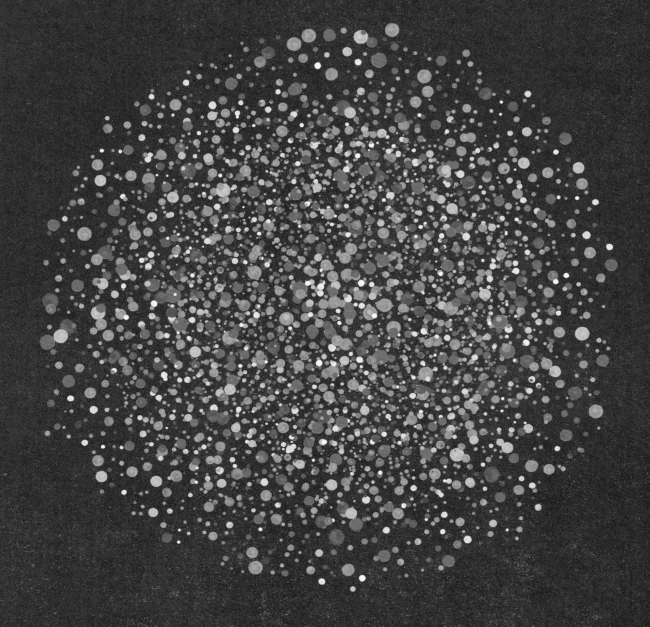

Eventually, so many particles stuck
together, that they started to make things.

At first they formed gigantic
dust clouds.

These dust clouds attracted more and more particles.

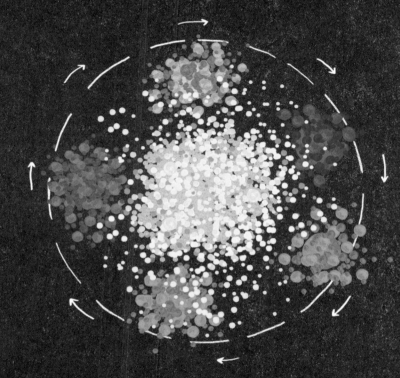

Over unfathomable lengths of time, they created suns.

And eventually, planets (who can't resist the pull of a good sun).

Home
sweet
home.

Our home planet is called Earth.

There we are, towards the middle of our
solar system. But Earth wasn't always
quite as homely as it is today.

At first, it was pretty warm around here.
But over time, the Earth began to cool.

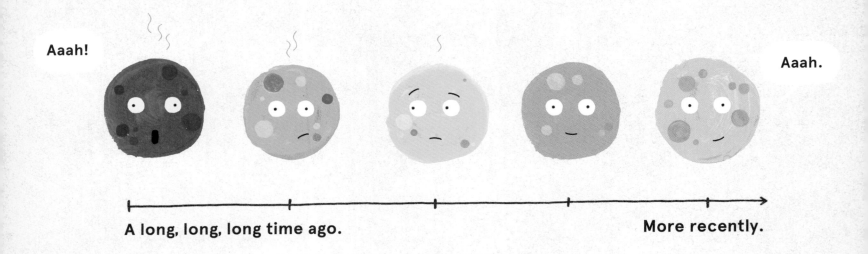

As our planet continued to cool, more and more
of those particles were drawn together.

More arrived from space, riding on meteors.

Some eventually became the land and water
on the Earth's surface.

Then one day, many moons ago,
the Earth was not too hot, and not too cold.
That warm water was just right for
the magic to happen.

And just like that, life came into existence.

The first life form was pretty simple. She couldn't see, hear, or wear a party hat. But she had one very special trick. She could make copies of herself.

Hello, handsome.

This is where all of our stories start. All life on Earth came from this single-celled being (you can think of her as your great, great, great – times a trillion, zillion, squillion – granny).

You, me, the trees, witchetty grubs, whales and wolves … we're all related to this little lady.

All of life is one.

She might have been simple, but your great granny[gazillion] was no slouch.

Through generations upon generations, her children (your ancestors) slowly adapted to make the most of life in the warm waters of our early Earth.

Nice to see you, dear.

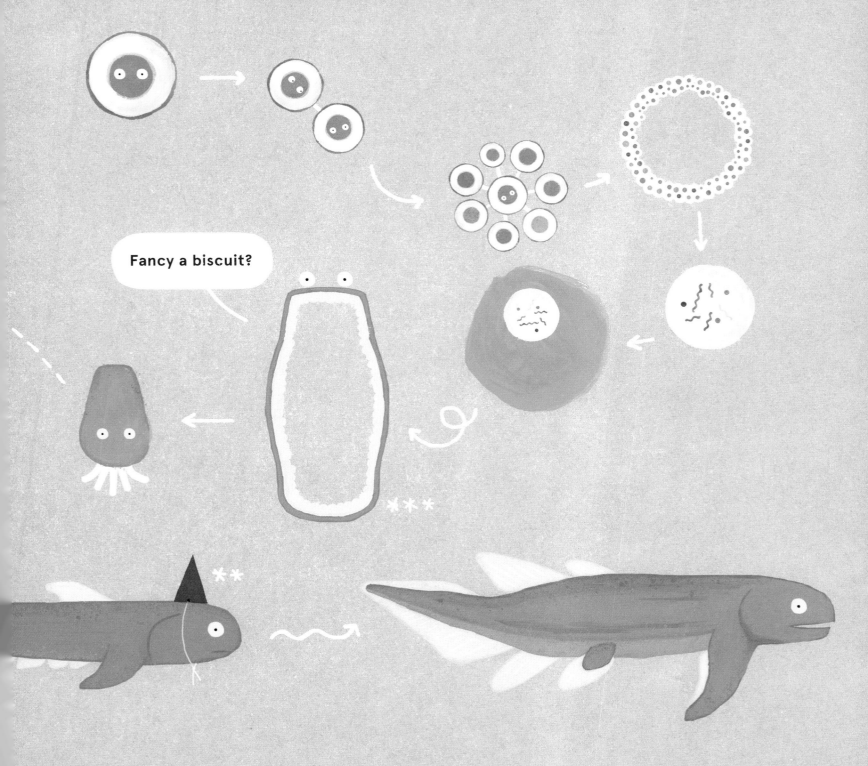

Very important small print:
(*) Our ancestors first developed eyes at about this stage in our journey. All peepers on creatures and creations before this point in the book have been gratuitously added for comic effect. (**) Party hat also added for comic effect. Maybe it's her birthday. (***) This guy's name was Bob.

Then one fine day, one particularly unassuming but industrious little fish decided to see what she could see, beyond the sea.

Her land-loving children would go on to become land animals. From dinosaurs to donkeys, yaks to you ... we can all trace our family tree back to this adventurous amphibian.

And of course, your evolutionary adventure didn't stop there. Over unimaginable lengths of time, our ancestors adapted to life on the land...

and then life
in the trees.

And from an ancestor we share with chimps,
we slowly evolved into the species we are today.

Humans.

The first humans lived in Africa,
but our sense of curiosity and adventure
soon took us to all corners of the Earth.

Wherever you live on the Earth, we are all descended from some very clever folks who lived right about here.

Except Antarctica.
We left that to the penguins.

Cheers.

We learned how
to farm.

Fire!

We built
communities.

And then towns,
and cities.

Then one night, only a few years ago,
some of those particles – that were
once part of stars, and the Earth,
and probably another life form
or two – became you.

Oh my.

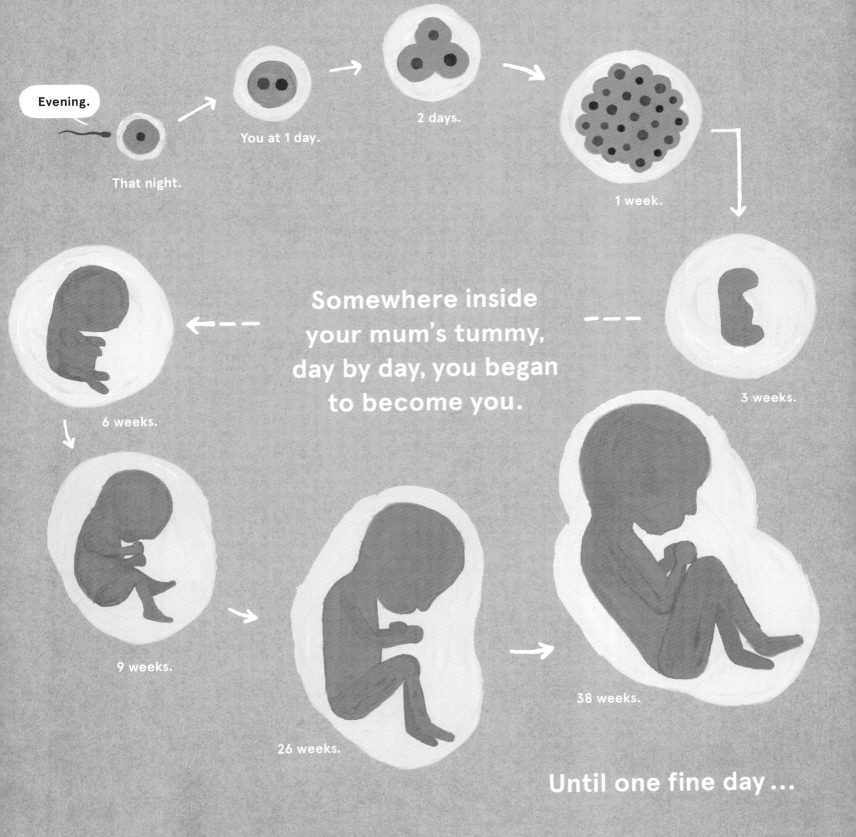

you made your grand entrance!

And that is how you got here.

You're very lucky to be here.

You are one of the newest additions to a family tree that goes all the way back to the very first life on Earth.

And just think, if any little thing had changed in the time after that first really, really, really big bang ...

you might have turned out a little different.

FOR MY MUM, CAROL,
WHO GOT ME HERE

Our universe is more unimaginably marvellous than we can ever suppose.
We know so little. There's still so much more to discover about how we got here,
and where we're going. One thing we do know, is that we humans only have one
home (you're sitting on it). It's yours to take care of. If you only do one thing with
this wild and beautiful life, make it your mission to leave the Earth (and everyone
that shares it with you) in better shape than they were when you got here.

Published in Great Britain
in 2019 by Wren & Rook

Copyright © Philip Bunting, 2018
Originally published by Scholastic
Australia Pty. Limited

The right of Philip Bunting to be
identified as the author of this Work has
been asserted by him in accordance
with the Copyright, Designs & Patents
Act 1988.

Hardback ISBN: 978 1 5263 6172 1
Paperback ISBN: 978 1 5263 6277 3
E-book ISBN: 978 1 5263 6215 5
10 9 8 7 6 5 4 3 2 1

FSC
www.fsc.org

MIX
Paper from
responsible sources
FSC® C104740

Wren & Rook
An imprint of Hachette Children's Group
Part of Hodder & Stoughton
Carmelite House
50 Victoria Embankment
London EC4Y 0DZ

An Hachette UK Company
www.hachette.co.uk
www.hachettechildrens.co.uk

Cover design by Laura Hambleton

Printed in China